Analogies

Analyzing Relationships
Between Words

Written by
Linda Schwartz

Editor: Kimberley Clark
Illustrator: Bev Armstrong
Cover Illustrator: Bev Armstrong
Designer: Clark Editorial and Design
Cover Designer: Barbara Peterson
Project Director: Carolea Williams

Special thanks to Chris Copeland, Cynthia Hofman, and Jennifer Almer for their input.

© 2002 Creative Teaching Press, Inc., Huntington Beach, CA 92649
Reproduction of activities in any manner for use in the classroom and not for commercial sale is permissible.
Reproduction of these materials for an entire school or for a school system is strictly prohibited.

Table of Contents

Introduction 3
What Is an Analogy? 4

Kinds of Analogies • 5–16

Analogy Overview 5–6
Synonyms and Antonyms #1 7
Synonyms and Antonyms #2 8
Homophones and Rhyming Words 9
Parts of a Whole and Groupings 10
Characteristics 11
How Things Are Used/Singular and Plural Spellings 12
Animal Groups and Offspring 13
Tools and Occupations/Things That Go Together 14
Analogy Review #1 15
Analogy Review #2 16

Science Analogies • 17–24

The Human Body 18
The Ocean 19
Fish 20
Birds 21
Mammals 22
Insects 23
Plants 24

Social Studies Analogies • 25–32

In the Neighborhood 26
Community Helpers 27
Transportation 28
Communication 29
Geography 30
Seasons and Celebrations 31
Homes 32

Just for Fun Analogies • 33–38

Things to Eat 34
School Days 35
Things to Wear 36
Playtime 37
Measuring, Counting, and Numbers 38

Resources • 39–48

Word Lists 40–41
Analogy Whizo Game 42
Analogy Whizo Word List 43
Analogy Whizo Game Card 44
Student Record Sheet 45
Analogy Awards 46
Answer Key 47–48

Introduction

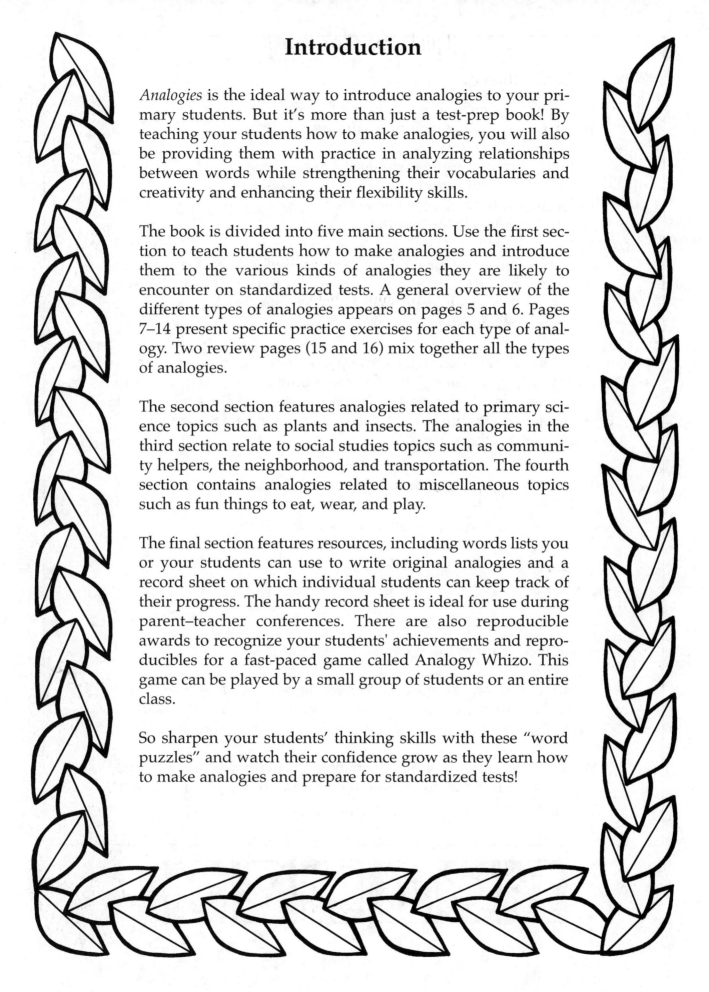

Analogies is the ideal way to introduce analogies to your primary students. But it's more than just a test-prep book! By teaching your students how to make analogies, you will also be providing them with practice in analyzing relationships between words while strengthening their vocabularies and creativity and enhancing their flexibility skills.

The book is divided into five main sections. Use the first section to teach students how to make analogies and introduce them to the various kinds of analogies they are likely to encounter on standardized tests. A general overview of the different types of analogies appears on pages 5 and 6. Pages 7–14 present specific practice exercises for each type of analogy. Two review pages (15 and 16) mix together all the types of analogies.

The second section features analogies related to primary science topics such as plants and insects. The analogies in the third section relate to social studies topics such as community helpers, the neighborhood, and transportation. The fourth section contains analogies related to miscellaneous topics such as fun things to eat, wear, and play.

The final section features resources, including words lists you or your students can use to write original analogies and a record sheet on which individual students can keep track of their progress. The handy record sheet is ideal for use during parent–teacher conferences. There are also reproducible awards to recognize your students' achievements and reproducibles for a fast-paced game called Analogy Whizo. This game can be played by a small group of students or an entire class.

So sharpen your students' thinking skills with these "word puzzles" and watch their confidence grow as they learn how to make analogies and prepare for standardized tests!

What Is an Analogy?

An *analogy* is a relationship between two pairs of words. Let's look at an example of an analogy.

<u>up</u> is to <u>down</u> as <u>hot</u> is to <u>cold</u>

The relationship between the first two words—<u>up</u> and <u>down</u> —is that they are *antonyms*, or opposites.

Look at the second pair of words—<u>hot</u> and <u>cold</u>. They are antonyms too. In order for the analogy to be correct, **both** pairs of words must be related in the **same way.** In this case, both pairs of words are antonyms, or opposites.

Now solve the analogy in the box below. Look at the first two words—<u>glad</u> and <u>happy</u>. They mean the same thing. Words that mean the same thing are called *synonyms*. Of the four word choices, which word means the **same thing** as loud? Fill in the bubble next to the word that best completes the analogy.

> <u>glad</u> is to <u>happy</u> as <u>loud</u> is to

- (a) quiet
- (b) crowd
- (c) light
- (d) noisy

If you picked answer **d**, <u>noisy</u>, you are right!

Choice **a** is wrong because *quiet* is the opposite of *loud*. Choice **b** is wrong because the word *crowd* rhymes with the word *loud*. Choice **c** is wrong because *light* does not mean the same as the word *loud*.

Work neatly when you fill in the bubbles. Stay inside the lines. If you change your mind about an answer, be sure to completely erase the wrong answer.

Analogy Overview

Here are some kinds of analogies you will be learning about in this book.

Analogies Using Synonyms
Synonyms are words that mean the same thing.

Example: <u>tiny</u> is to <u>small</u> as <u>big</u> is to <u>huge</u>

Analogies Using Antonyms
Antonyms are words that have opposite meanings.

Example: <u>happy</u> is to <u>sad</u> as <u>yes</u> is to <u>no</u>

Analogies Using Homophones
Homophones are words that sound the same but are spelled differently and have different meanings.

Example: <u>flower</u> is to <u>flour</u> as <u>blue</u> is to <u>blew</u>

Analogies Using Rhyming Words

Example: <u>house</u> is to <u>mouse</u> as <u>chair</u> is to <u>hair</u>

Analogies Using General Groups and Specific Members of Those Groups (or specific members of a group and the general group)

Examples: <u>oriole</u> is to <u>bird</u> as <u>elm</u> is to <u>tree</u>

<u>flower</u> is to <u>rose</u> as <u>mammal</u> is to <u>horse</u>

Analogies Using Parts of a Whole

Example: <u>eye</u> is to <u>head</u> as <u>finger</u> is to <u>hand</u>

In this example, an eye is found on a head and a finger is found on a hand.

Analogy Overview

Here are some more kinds of analogies you will be learning about in this book.

Analogies Using Characteristics That Describe What the First Word Looks Like

Example: <u>sun</u> is to <u>yellow</u> as <u>sky</u> is to <u>blue</u>

Analogies That Compare How Things Are Used

Example: <u>ruler</u> is to <u>measure</u> as <u>scissors</u> is to <u>cut</u>

Analogies with Singular and Plural Spellings of Words
Remember that singular means *one* and plural means *more than one*.

Example: <u>dog</u> is to <u>dogs</u> as <u>bench</u> is to <u>benches</u>

Analogies That Compare Animal Groups
Analogies That Compare Animal Offspring or Young

Examples: <u>herd</u> is to <u>horses</u> as <u>swarm</u> is to <u>bees</u>

        <u>chicken</u> is to <u>chick</u> as <u>kangaroo</u> is to <u>joey</u>

Analogies That Relate Tools to the People Who Use Them

Example: <u>hammer</u> is to <u>carpenter</u> as <u>ax</u> is to <u>firefighter</u>

Analogies That Compare Things That Usually Go Together

Example: <u>salt</u> is to <u>pepper</u> as <u>peanut butter</u> is to <u>jelly</u>

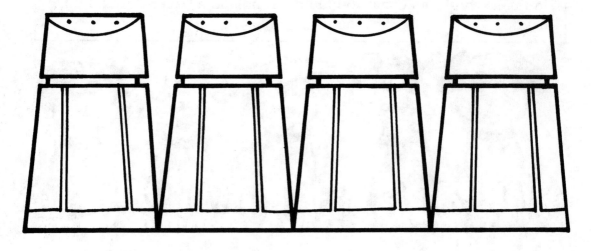

Analogies © 2002 Creative Teaching Press

Synonyms and Antonyms #1

Words that mean the **same** thing are called *synonyms*.

Example: <u>ill</u> and <u>sick</u>

Words that mean the **opposite** of each other are called *antonyms*.

Example: <u>open</u> and <u>close</u>

Here are some analogies with synonyms and antonyms. Decide if the first pair of words is alike (synonyms) or opposite (antonyms).
Fill in the bubble next to the word that best completes each analogy.

1. <u>false</u> is to <u>untrue</u> as <u>late</u> is to
   - (a) first
   - (b) early
   - (c) date
   - (d) tardy

2. <u>few</u> is to <u>many</u> as <u>open</u> is to
   - (a) closed
   - (b) door
   - (c) empty
   - (d) wide

3. <u>below</u> is to <u>above</u> as <u>old</u> is to
   - (a) rotten
   - (b) bold
   - (c) new
   - (d) worn

4. <u>night</u> is to <u>day</u> as <u>in</u> is to
   - (a) near
   - (b) bin
   - (c) inn
   - (d) out

5. <u>hard</u> is to <u>soft</u> as <u>crooked</u> is to
   - (a) cracked
   - (b) straight
   - (c) teeth
   - (d) wavy

6. <u>strong</u> is to <u>mighty</u> as <u>timid</u> is to
   - (a) happy
   - (b) tiny
   - (c) brave
   - (d) shy

7. <u>wrong</u> is to <u>right</u> as <u>tall</u> is to
   - (a) mall
   - (b) high
   - (c) short
   - (d) giraffe

8. <u>big</u> is to <u>huge</u> as <u>kind</u> is to
   - (a) mind
   - (b) mean
   - (c) nice
   - (d) funny

Synonyms and Antonyms #2

Fill in the bubble next to the word that best completes each analogy.

1. off is to on as high is to
   - (a) top
   - (b) low
   - (c) by
   - (d) tall

2. foolish is to wise as weak is to
   - (a) strong
   - (b) week
   - (c) shy
   - (d) unhealthy

3. fast is to slow as far is to
   - (a) for
   - (b) away
   - (c) tar
   - (d) near

4. plain is to fancy as alike is to
   - (a) almost
   - (b) same
   - (c) different
   - (d) similar

5. blend is to mix as search is to
   - (a) hide
   - (b) sear
   - (c) perch
   - (d) seek

6. shiny is to dull as heavy is to
   - (a) weight
   - (b) light
   - (c) ton
   - (d) thick

7. easy is to simple as fix is to
   - (a) six
   - (b) break
   - (c) destroy
   - (d) repair

8. empty is to vacant as damp is to
   - (a) dry
   - (b) camp
   - (c) moist
   - (d) danger

Analogies © 2002 Creative Teaching Press

Homophones and Rhyming Words

> *Homophones* are words that sound the same
> but are spelled differently and mean different things.
> Example: <u>ate</u> and <u>eight</u>
>
> *Rhyming words* have the same ending sounds
> but different beginning sounds.
> Example: <u>bat</u> and <u>cat</u>

Here are some analogies with homophones and rhyming words.
Fill in the bubble next to the word that best completes each analogy.

1. <u>toe</u> is to <u>tow</u> as <u>pail</u> is to
   - (a) tale
   - (b) beach
   - (c) pale
   - (d) shovel

2. <u>chair</u> is to <u>care</u> as <u>log</u> is to
   - (a) lumber
   - (b) wood
   - (c) dog
   - (d) leg

3. <u>made</u> is to <u>maid</u> as <u>tied</u> is to
   - (a) tide
   - (b) shoe
   - (c) hide
   - (d) lace

4. <u>been</u> is to <u>bin</u> as <u>due</u> is to
   - (a) two
   - (b) dew
   - (c) doe
   - (d) few

5. <u>not</u> is to <u>knot</u> as <u>piece</u> is to
   - (a) place
   - (b) niece
   - (c) peace
   - (d) pie

6. <u>rest</u> is to <u>best</u> as <u>pan</u> is to
   - (a) man
   - (b) pot
   - (c) cook
   - (d) pen

7. <u>flake</u> is to <u>quake</u> as <u>spend</u> is to
   - (a) money
   - (b) mend
   - (c) cost
   - (d) save

8. <u>board</u> is to <u>bored</u> as <u>deer</u> is to
   - (a) mammal
   - (b) dear
   - (c) dream
   - (d) animal

Analogies © 2002 Creative Teaching Press

Name _____

Parts of a Whole and Groupings

Fill in the bubble next to the word that best completes each analogy.

1. student is to class as singer is to
   - (a) ringer
   - (b) singers
   - (c) choir
   - (d) song

2. rabbit is to mammal as dove is to
   - (a) love
   - (b) bird
   - (c) parrot
   - (d) fish

3. player is to team as scout is to
   - (a) troop
   - (b) pout
   - (c) scoot
   - (d) find

4. bulb is to lamp as lens is to
   - (a) look
   - (b) chair
   - (c) camera
   - (d) table

5. insect is to beetle as fish is to
   - (a) wish
   - (b) shark
   - (c) stream
   - (d) dinosaur

6. heel is to foot as palm is to
   - (a) head
   - (b) chest
   - (c) back
   - (d) hand

7. wrist is to arm as ankle is to
   - (a) shoulder
   - (b) neck
   - (c) waist
   - (d) leg

8. guitar is to string as piano is to
   - (a) key
   - (b) music
   - (c) song
   - (d) violin

Characteristics

Fill in the bubble next to the word that best completes each analogy.

1. <u>tomato</u> is to <u>red</u> as <u>lettuce</u> is to
   - (a) orange
   - (b) salad
   - (c) yellow
   - (d) green

2. <u>fire</u> is to <u>hot</u> as <u>ice</u> is to
   - (a) soda
   - (b) cold
   - (c) freezer
   - (d) cream

3. <u>large</u> is to <u>elephant</u> as <u>small</u> is to
   - (a) big
   - (b) dinosaur
   - (c) ant
   - (d) tiny

4. <u>lung</u> is to <u>human</u> as <u>fin</u> is to
   - (a) fish
   - (b) hill
   - (c) flower
   - (d) horse

5. <u>feather</u> is to <u>soft</u> as <u>brick</u> is to
   - (a) hard
   - (b) house
   - (c) trick
   - (d) gray

6. <u>candy</u> is to <u>sweet</u> as <u>lemon</u> is to
   - (a) fruit
   - (b) sour
   - (c) hot
   - (d) round

7. <u>horse</u> is to <u>mane</u> as <u>turtle</u> is to
   - (a) snail
   - (b) green
   - (c) slow
   - (d) shell

8. <u>siren</u> is to <u>loud</u> as <u>whisper</u> is to
   - (a) scream
   - (b) cry
   - (c) quiet
   - (d) shout

Analogies © 2002 Creative Teaching Press

How Things Are Used/Singular and Plural Spellings

Fill in the bubble next to the word that best completes each analogy.

1. sweep is to broom as cut is to
   - (a) but
   - (b) cuts
   - (c) knife
   - (d) paper

2. man is to men as woman is to
   - (a) lady
   - (b) mother
   - (c) male
   - (d) women

3. hero is to heroes as box is to
   - (a) fox
   - (b) boxes
   - (c) cardboard
   - (d) square

4. clock is to time as thermometer is to
   - (a) speed
   - (b) month
   - (c) temperature
   - (d) depth

5. fire is to heat as lamp is to
   - (a) house
   - (b) light
   - (c) camp
   - (d) flashlight

6. ax is to chop as scissors is to
   - (a) paste
   - (b) color
   - (c) cut
   - (d) sword

7. shovel is to dig as spoon is to
   - (a) moon
   - (b) fork
   - (c) kitchen
   - (d) stir

8. wallet is to money as notebook is to
   - (a) globe
   - (b) paper
   - (c) house
   - (d) desk

Analogies © 2002 Creative Teaching Press

Name _____

Animal Groups and Offspring

Fill in the bubble next to the word that best completes each analogy.

1. <u>calf</u> is to <u>elephant</u> as <u>piglet</u> is to
   - (a) pink
   - (b) pig
   - (c) sheep
   - (d) goat

2. <u>flock</u> is to <u>chicken</u> as <u>school</u> is to
   - (a) rule
   - (b) rabbit
   - (c) peacocks
   - (d) fish

3. <u>cub</u> is to <u>wolf</u> as <u>lamb</u> is to
   - (a) sheep
   - (b) turkey
   - (c) oyster
   - (d) fox

4. <u>cat</u> is to <u>kitten</u> as <u>eagle</u> is to
   - (a) fish
   - (b) plant
   - (c) pack
   - (d) eaglet

5. <u>duckling</u> is to <u>duck</u> as <u>fawn</u> is to
   - (a) dawn
   - (b) horse
   - (c) buffalo
   - (d) deer

6. <u>dog</u> is to <u>pack</u> as <u>ant</u> is to
   - (a) fall
   - (b) colony
   - (c) drove
   - (d) troop

7. <u>gosling</u> is to <u>goose</u> as <u>cub</u> is to
   - (a) goat
   - (b) tub
   - (c) lion
   - (d) donkey

8. <u>pod</u> is to <u>whales</u> as <u>herd</u> is to
   - (a) monkey
   - (b) cattle
   - (c) cat
   - (d) otter

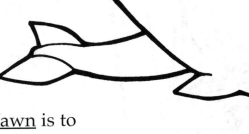

Analogies © 2002 Creative Teaching Press

Name _____

Tools and Occupations/Things That Go Together

Fill in the bubble next to the word that best completes each analogy.

1. <u>bat</u> is to <u>ball</u> as <u>key</u> is to
   - (a) metal
   - (b) see
   - (c) lock
   - (d) silver

2. <u>stamp</u> is to <u>envelope</u> as <u>needle</u> is to
   - (a) thread
   - (b) sharp
   - (c) sew
   - (d) point

3. <u>computer</u> is to <u>secretary</u> as <u>violin</u> is to
   - (a) harp
   - (b) musician
   - (c) drum
   - (d) music

4. <u>farmer</u> is to <u>hoe</u> as <u>swimmer</u> is to
   - (a) water
   - (b) goggles
   - (c) diver
   - (d) dimmer

5. <u>bacon</u> is to <u>eggs</u> as <u>salt</u> is to
   - (a) pepper
   - (b) malt
   - (c) white
   - (d) spice

6. <u>cake</u> is to <u>ice cream</u> as <u>toast</u> is to
   - (a) bread
   - (b) boast
   - (c) jelly
   - (d) meat

7. <u>saucer</u> is to <u>cup</u> as <u>shoe</u> is to
   - (a) few
   - (b) walk
   - (c) sock
   - (d) boot

8. <u>custodian</u> is to <u>broom</u> as <u>gardener</u> is to
   - (a) whistle
   - (b) hose
   - (c) bush
   - (d) lamp

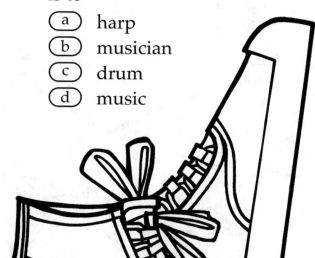

Analogies © 2002 Creative Teaching Press

Name _____

Analogy Review #1

Fill in the bubble next to the word that best completes each analogy.

1. insect is to grasshopper as bird is to
   - (a) third
   - (b) snake
   - (c) trout
   - (d) parrot

2. float is to sink as follow is to
   - (a) copy
   - (b) fellow
   - (c) hollow
   - (d) lead

3. water is to liquid as air is to
   - (a) gas
   - (b) care
   - (c) cloud
   - (d) solid

4. flower is to garden as tree is to
   - (a) trunk
   - (b) three
   - (c) forest
   - (d) green

5. stair is to stare as their is to
   - (a) those
   - (b) there
   - (c) them
   - (d) that

6. girl is to boy as woman is to
   - (a) female
   - (b) mother
   - (c) lady
   - (d) man

7. roar is to lion as bark is to
   - (a) cat
   - (b) dog
   - (c) sheep
   - (d) tiger

8. under is to over as sharp is to
   - (a) smart
   - (b) dull
   - (c) harp
   - (d) point

Analogies © 2002 Creative Teaching Press

Name _____

Analogy Review #2

Fill in the bubble next to the word that best completes each analogy.

1. <u>pedal</u> is to <u>bike</u> as <u>row</u> is to
   - (a) boat
   - (b) grow
   - (c) paddle
   - (d) line

2. <u>chew</u> is to <u>mouth</u> as <u>hear</u> is to
   - (a) eye
   - (b) smell
   - (c) ear
   - (d) teeth

3. <u>answer</u> is to <u>question</u> as <u>solve</u> is to
   - (a) add
   - (b) time
   - (c) feeling
   - (d) problem

4. <u>calm</u> is to <u>excited</u> as <u>join</u> is to
   - (a) connect
   - (b) separate
   - (c) together
   - (d) coin

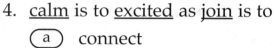

5. <u>bow</u> is to <u>arrow</u> as <u>hammer</u> is to
   - (a) knife
   - (b) nail
   - (c) tool
   - (d) slammer

6. <u>thing</u> is to <u>swing</u> as <u>change</u> is to
   - (a) money
   - (b) coin
   - (c) improve
   - (d) range

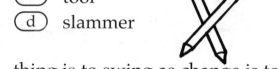

7. <u>pair</u> is to <u>two</u> as <u>dozen</u> is to
   - (a) twelve
   - (b) eggs
   - (c) six
   - (d) ten

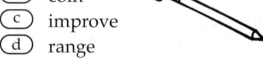

8. <u>sleeve</u> is to <u>shirt</u> as <u>heel</u> is to
   - (a) heal
   - (b) steel
   - (c) belt
   - (d) shoe

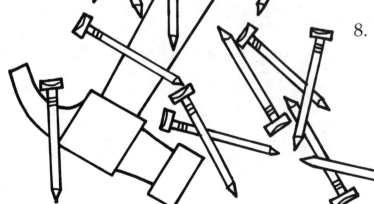

Analogies © 2002 Creative Teaching Press

Science Analogies

Name _____

The Human Body

Fill in the bubble next to the word that best completes each analogy.

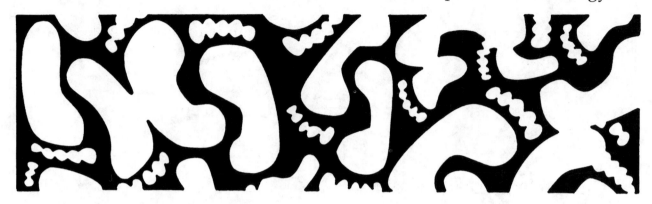

1. teeth is to tooth as feet is to
    - (a) foot
    - (b) toe
    - (c) feets
    - (d) shoe

2. eye is to sight as ear is to
    - (a) smell
    - (b) tear
    - (c) taste
    - (d) sound

3. toe is to foot as thumb is to
    - (a) arm
    - (b) joint
    - (c) hand
    - (d) skull

4. hair is to head as nail is to
    - (a) knee
    - (b) finger
    - (c) iris
    - (d) joint

5. bone is to tone as blood is to
    - (a) red
    - (b) vein
    - (c) flood
    - (d) eye

6. knee is to leg as elbow is to
    - (a) chest
    - (b) ankle
    - (c) head
    - (d) arm

7. eye is to I as hair is to
    - (a) brush
    - (b) hare
    - (c) curly
    - (d) scalp

8. nose is to one as ears is to
    - (a) two
    - (b) hears
    - (c) three
    - (d) sound

Analogies © 2002 Creative Teaching Pre

The Ocean

Fill in the bubble next to the word that best completes each analogy.

1. <u>sea</u> is to <u>see</u> as <u>beach</u> is to
   - (a) ball
   - (b) beech
   - (c) sand
   - (d) ocean

2. <u>calm</u> is to <u>peaceful</u> as <u>fast</u> is to
   - (a) quick
   - (b) first
   - (c) slow
   - (d) past

3. <u>tide</u> is to <u>hide</u> as <u>wave</u> is to
   - (a) ripple
   - (b) peak
   - (c) greet
   - (d) gave

4. <u>ocean</u> is to <u>fish</u> as <u>sky</u> is to
   - (a) whale
   - (b) bird
   - (c) tiger
   - (d) blue

5. <u>deep</u> is to <u>shallow</u> as <u>narrow</u> is to
   - (a) thin
   - (b) near
   - (c) wide
   - (d) skinny

6. <u>ocean</u> is to <u>blue</u> as <u>grass</u> is to
   - (a) lawn
   - (b) dirt
   - (c) green
   - (d) blade

7. <u>shell</u> is to <u>oyster</u> as <u>peel</u> is to
   - (a) banana
   - (b) peal
   - (c) open
   - (d) reel

8. <u>canoe</u> is to <u>boat</u> as <u>ballet</u> is to
   - (a) tap
   - (b) dance
   - (c) stage
   - (d) music

Analogies © 2002 Creative Teaching Press

Fish

Fill in the bubble next to the word that best completes each analogy.

1. <u>gill</u> is to <u>fish</u> as <u>lung</u> is to
   - (a) ant
   - (b) human
   - (c) lungs
   - (d) rung

2. <u>large</u> is to <u>small</u> as <u>many</u> is to
   - (a) most
   - (b) number
   - (c) huge
   - (d) few

3. <u>shark</u> is to <u>sharks</u> as <u>man</u> is to
   - (a) male
   - (b) men
   - (c) mister
   - (d) lady

4. <u>trout</u> is to <u>spout</u> as <u>sea</u> is to
   - (a) seaweed
   - (b) ocean
   - (c) flea
   - (d) stout

5. <u>scale</u> is to <u>fish</u> as <u>feather</u> is to
   - (a) soft
   - (b) leather
   - (c) snake
   - (d) bird

6. <u>clam</u> is to <u>ham</u> as <u>eel</u> is to
   - (a) lizard
   - (b) eels
   - (c) cod
   - (d) peel

7. <u>fin</u> is to <u>shark</u> as <u>pouch</u> is to
   - (a) pouches
   - (b) grouch
   - (c) kangaroo
   - (d) ostrich

8. <u>goldfish</u> is to <u>orange</u> as <u>flamingo</u> is to
   - (a) blue
   - (b) pink
   - (c) green
   - (d) yellow

Analogies © 2002 Creative Teaching Press

Name _____

Birds

Fill in the bubble next to the word that best completes each analogy.

1. sparrow is to bird as salmon is to
   - (a) vegetable
   - (b) mammal
   - (c) fish
   - (d) reptile

2. beak is to parrot as mouth is to
   - (a) taste
   - (b) human
   - (c) tongue
   - (d) eye

3. canary is to yellow as crow is to
   - (a) green
   - (b) blue
   - (c) black
   - (d) purple

4. bird is to nest as bee is to
   - (a) hive
   - (b) ant
   - (c) be
   - (d) fly

5. chick is to chicken as colt is to
   - (a) horse
   - (b) camel
   - (c) whale
   - (d) fox

6. feather is to weather as cage is to
   - (a) pen
   - (b) metal
   - (c) home
   - (d) page

7. loud is to soft as rude is to
   - (a) mean
   - (b) nasty
   - (c) polite
   - (d) sharp

8. duck is to duckling as hog is to
   - (a) jog
   - (b) piglet
   - (c) hogs
   - (d) filly

Analogies © 2002 Creative Teaching Press

Mammals

Fill in the bubble next to the word that best completes each analogy.

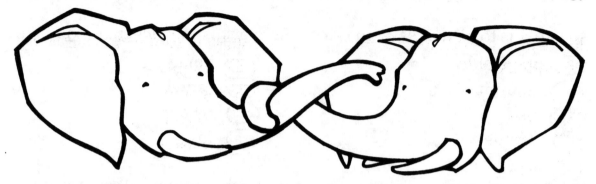

1. <u>zebra</u> is to <u>stripes</u> as <u>leopard</u> is to
   - (a) animal
   - (b) horse
   - (c) jungle
   - (d) spots

2. <u>kitten</u> is to <u>cat</u> as <u>puppy</u> is to
   - (a) cub
   - (b) dog
   - (c) tail
   - (d) colt

3. <u>mane</u> is to <u>lion</u> as <u>hump</u> is to
   - (a) bump
   - (b) rabbit
   - (c) monkey
   - (d) camel

4. <u>fox</u> is to <u>foxes</u> as <u>mouse</u> is to
   - (a) mouses
   - (b) mousies
   - (c) mice
   - (d) mices

5. <u>whale</u> is to <u>ocean</u> as <u>bat</u> is to
   - (a) hat
   - (b) cave
   - (c) sand
   - (d) wings

6. <u>human</u> is to <u>nose</u> as <u>elephant</u> is to
   - (a) trunk
   - (b) foot
   - (c) gray
   - (d) mammal

7. <u>bear</u> is to <u>bare</u> as <u>tail</u> is to
   - (a) mammal
   - (b) wail
   - (c) tale
   - (d) ear

8. <u>fawn</u> is to <u>deer</u> as <u>cub</u> is to
   - (a) pig
   - (b) kangaroo
   - (c) lion
   - (d) tub

Analogies © 2002 Creative Teaching Press

Insects

Fill in the bubble next to the word that best completes each analogy.

1. <u>caterpillar</u> is to <u>butterfly</u> as <u>tadpole</u> is to
   - (a) fish
   - (b) frog
   - (c) lake
   - (d) toad

2. <u>insect</u> is to <u>ladybug</u> as <u>reptile</u> is to
   - (a) owl
   - (b) horse
   - (c) alligator
   - (d) iris

3. <u>mosquito</u> is to <u>buzz</u> as <u>rooster</u> is to
   - (a) hen
   - (b) egg
   - (c) booster
   - (d) crow

4. <u>ant</u> is to <u>aunt</u> as <u>bee</u> is to
   - (a) bug
   - (b) be
   - (c) tee
   - (d) wasp

5. <u>bug</u> is to <u>dug</u> as <u>cricket</u> is to
   - (a) night
   - (b) game
   - (c) ticket
   - (d) racket

6. <u>feelers</u> is to <u>antennae</u> as <u>fast</u> is to
   - (a) quick
   - (b) past
   - (c) slow
   - (d) crawl

7. <u>grasshopper</u> is to <u>jump</u> as <u>snake</u> is to
   - (a) fly
   - (b) lizard
   - (c) reptile
   - (d) crawl

8. <u>moth</u> is to <u>moths</u> as <u>roach</u> is to
   - (a) beetle
   - (b) roaches
   - (c) poach
   - (d) termite

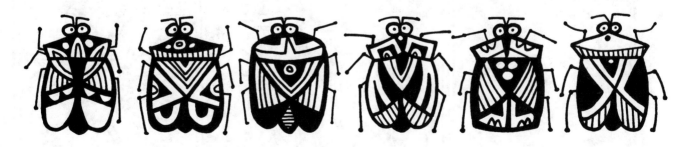

Analogies © 2002 Creative Teaching Press

Plants

Fill in the bubble next to the word that best completes each analogy.

1. petal is to flower as finger is to
   - (a) ring
   - (b) foot
   - (c) hand
   - (d) neck

2. root is to boot as stem is to
   - (a) soil
   - (b) hem
   - (c) branch
   - (d) trunk

3. small is to tiny as odor is to
   - (a) large
   - (b) cheese
   - (c) sound
   - (d) smell

4. oak is to tree as pear is to
   - (a) fruit
   - (b) apple
   - (c) vegetable
   - (d) meat

5. rose is to nose as pine is to
   - (a) cone
   - (b) line
   - (c) tree
   - (d) evergreen

6. plant is to leaf as chair is to
   - (a) couch
   - (b) table
   - (c) hair
   - (d) leg

7. cactus is to desert as seaweed is to
   - (a) plant
   - (b) fish
   - (c) tree
   - (d) ocean

8. gardener is to rake as artist is to
   - (a) teacher
   - (b) cartoon
   - (c) brush
   - (d) food

Analogies © 2002 Creative Teaching Press

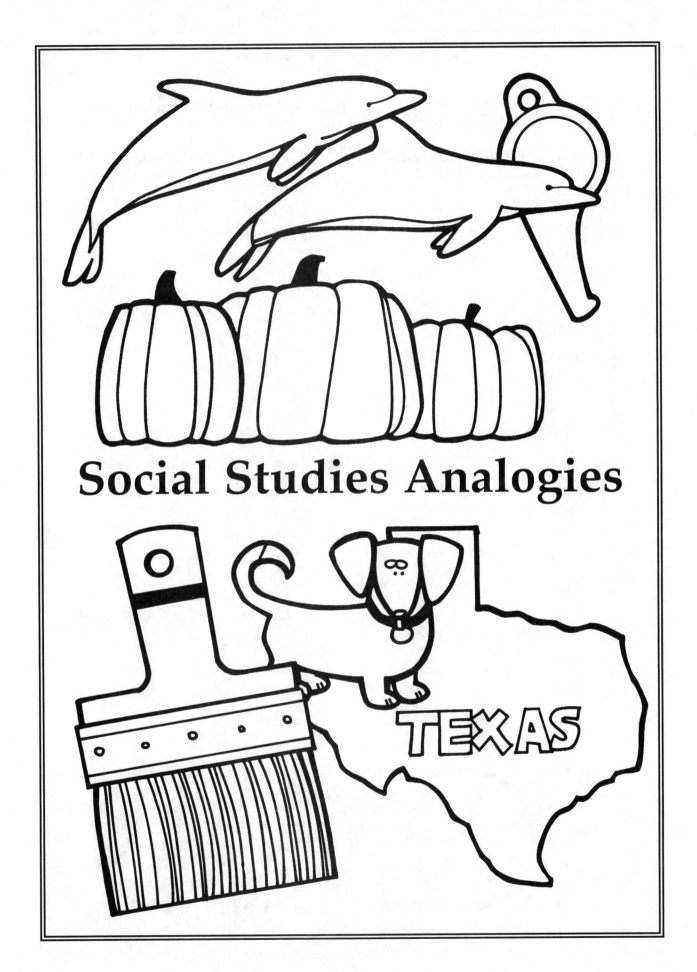

Social Studies Analogies

Name _____

In the Neighborhood

Fill in the bubble next to the word that best completes each analogy.

1. <u>court</u> is to <u>basketball</u> as <u>diamond</u> is to
   - (a) square
   - (b) baseball
   - (c) circle
   - (d) shiny

2. <u>car</u> is to <u>road</u> as <u>train</u> is to
   - (a) engine
   - (b) brain
   - (c) track
   - (d) whistle

3. <u>friend</u> is to <u>pal</u> as <u>woman</u> is to
   - (a) lady
   - (b) male
   - (c) child
   - (d) mayor

4. <u>quiet</u> is to <u>noisy</u> as <u>clean</u> is to
   - (a) neat
   - (b) messy
   - (c) tidy
   - (d) wash

5. <u>gate</u> is to <u>fence</u> as <u>door</u> is to
   - (a) window
   - (b) tree
   - (c) doors
   - (d) house

6. <u>mow</u> is to <u>grass</u> as <u>recycle</u> is to
   - (a) hose
   - (b) bench
   - (c) paper
   - (d) sing

7. <u>book</u> is to <u>library</u> as <u>money</u> is to
   - (a) dollar
   - (b) cash
   - (c) saving
   - (d) bank

8. <u>asleep</u> is to <u>awake</u> as <u>tight</u> is to
   - (a) loose
   - (b) might
   - (c) crowded
   - (d) rigid

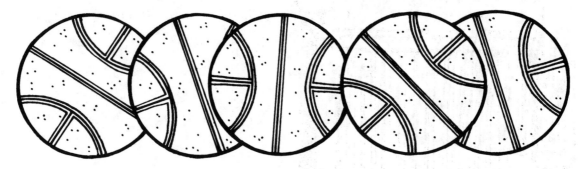

Analogies © 2002 Creative Teaching Press

Name _____

Community Helpers

Fill in the bubble next to the word that best completes each analogy.

1. <u>barber</u> is to <u>scissors</u> as <u>nurse</u> is to
   - a) doctor
   - b) rake
   - c) thermometer
   - d) office

2. <u>work</u> is to <u>play</u> as <u>open</u> is to
   - a) door
   - b) wide
   - c) window
   - d) shut

3. <u>doctor</u> is to <u>hospital</u> as <u>teacher</u> is to
   - a) book
   - b) desk
   - c) school
   - d) lesson

4. <u>firefighter</u> is to <u>ladder</u> as <u>author</u> is to
   - a) actor
   - b) computer
   - c) hammer
   - d) movie

5. <u>painter</u> is to <u>fainter</u> as <u>judge</u> is to
   - a) court
   - b) jury
   - c) fudge
   - d) trial

6. <u>chef</u> is to <u>food</u> as <u>florist</u> is to
   - a) flowers
   - b) jewelry
   - c) hair
   - d) reptiles

7. <u>dentist</u> is to <u>teeth</u> as <u>vet</u> is to
   - a) buildings
   - b) cars
   - c) flowers
   - d) animals

8. <u>job</u> is to <u>task</u> as <u>piece</u> is to
   - a) peace
   - b) part
   - c) pie
   - d) niece

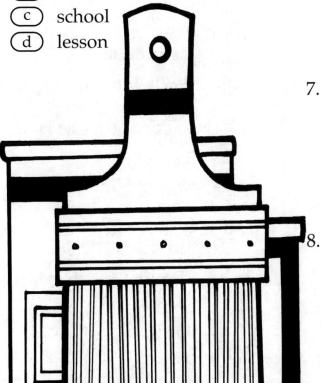

Analogies © 2002 Creative Teaching Press

Name _____

Transportation

Fill in the bubble next to the word or words that best completes each analogy.

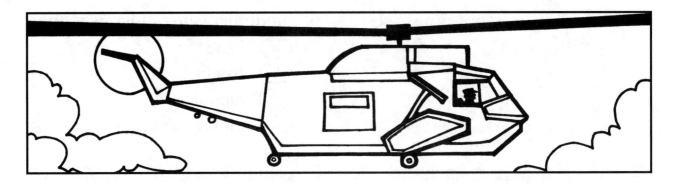

1. <u>wagon</u> is to <u>dragon</u> as <u>car</u> is to
   - (a) driver
   - (b) scooter
   - (c) bus
   - (d) far

2. <u>raft</u> is to <u>river</u> as <u>helicopter</u> is to
   - (a) sky
   - (b) ship
   - (c) blade
   - (d) blimp

3. <u>ship</u> is to <u>boat</u> as <u>jet</u> is to
   - (a) train
   - (b) plane
   - (c) cab
   - (d) get

4. <u>arrive</u> is to <u>depart</u> as <u>stay</u> is to
   - (a) play
   - (b) stare
   - (c) stays
   - (d) leave

5. <u>driver</u> is to <u>car</u> as <u>pilot</u> is to
   - (a) school bus
   - (b) pilots
   - (c) airplane
   - (d) ambulance

6. <u>track</u> is to <u>train</u> as <u>road</u> is to
   - (a) rode
   - (b) toad
   - (c) motorcycle
   - (d) submarine

7. <u>cab</u> is to <u>tab</u> as <u>tricycle</u> is to
   - (a) bicycle
   - (b) automobile
   - (c) wagon
   - (d) skateboard

8. <u>truck</u> is to <u>trucks</u> as <u>bus</u> is to
   - (a) city
   - (b) buses
   - (c) fuss
   - (d) school

Analogies © 2002 Creative Teaching Press

Name _____

Communication

Fill in the bubble next to the word that best completes each analogy.

1. <u>mail</u> is to <u>male</u> as <u>seam</u> is to
   - (a) dress
   - (b) sew
   - (c) seem
   - (d) ream

2. <u>letter</u> is to <u>mailbox</u> as <u>e-mail</u> is to
   - (a) stamp
   - (b) keyboard
   - (c) computer
   - (d) mouse

3. <u>read</u> is to <u>book</u> as <u>listen</u> is to
   - (a) painting
   - (b) radio
   - (c) ear
   - (d) glisten

4. <u>letter</u> is to <u>envelope</u> as <u>gift</u> is to
   - (a) box
   - (b) lift
   - (c) present
   - (d) ribbon

5. <u>watch</u> is to <u>watches</u> as <u>baby</u> is to
   - (a) babies
   - (b) adult
   - (c) child
   - (d) babys

6. <u>mouth</u> is to <u>talk</u> as <u>ear</u> is to
   - (a) head
   - (b) listen
   - (c) face
   - (d) noise

7. <u>drum</u> is to <u>beat</u> as <u>whistle</u> is to
   - (a) soccer
   - (b) coach
   - (c) blow
   - (d) bell

8. <u>umpire</u> is to <u>baseball</u> as <u>referee</u> is to
   - (a) dance
   - (b) signal
   - (c) sport
   - (d) football

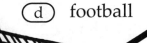

Analogies © 2002 Creative Teaching Press

Geography

Fill in the bubble next to the word that best completes each analogy.

1. north is to south as east is to
   - (a) beast
   - (b) find
   - (c) globe
   - (d) west

2. near is to close as sleepy is to
   - (a) tired
   - (b) bed
   - (c) awake
   - (d) night

3. map is to tap as lake is to
   - (a) island
   - (b) fish
   - (c) take
   - (d) swim

4. peak is to peek as cent is to
   - (a) penny
   - (b) money
   - (c) sent
   - (d) coin

5. Boston is to city as Texas is to
   - (a) mountain
   - (b) lake
   - (c) river
   - (d) state

6. plain is to plane as sew is to
   - (a) so
   - (b) needle
   - (c) thread
   - (d) blow

7. atlas is to map as dictionary is to
   - (a) word
   - (b) puzzle
   - (c) game
   - (d) report

8. desert is to hot as arctic is to
   - (a) penguin
   - (b) cold
   - (c) steam
   - (d) forest

Analogies © 2002 Creative Teaching Press

Name _____

Seasons and Celebrations

Fill in the bubble next to the word that best completes each analogy.

1. snow is to winter as rain is to
   - (a) water
   - (b) spring
   - (c) drain
   - (d) umbrella

2. Thanksgiving is to November as Valentine's Day is to
   - (a) December
   - (b) heart
   - (c) candy
   - (d) February

3. pumpkin is to orange as corn is to
   - (a) cob
   - (b) brown
   - (c) purple
   - (d) yellow

4. hot is to cold as part is to
   - (a) fraction
   - (b) whole
   - (c) hair
   - (d) smart

5. sleigh is to slay as night is to
   - (a) knight
   - (b) day
   - (c) dark
   - (d) moon

6. march is to parade as sing is to
   - (a) ring
   - (b) dance
   - (c) choir
   - (d) laugh

7. costume is to body as mask is to
   - (a) face
   - (b) scary
   - (c) leg
   - (d) hide

8. July is to summer as December is to
   - (a) January
   - (b) month
   - (c) week
   - (d) winter

Name _____

Homes

Fill in the bubble next to the word that best completes each analogy.

1. <u>igloo</u> is to <u>ice</u> as <u>cabin</u> is to
   - (a) store
   - (b) apartment
   - (c) logs
   - (d) hotel

2. <u>house</u> is to <u>home</u> as <u>coat</u> is to
   - (a) note
   - (b) button
   - (c) jacket
   - (d) night

3. <u>robin</u> is to <u>tree</u> as <u>salmon</u> is to
   - (a) grass
   - (b) river
   - (c) mountain
   - (d) tree

4. <u>bat</u> is to <u>cave</u> as <u>lion</u> is to
   - (a) pond
   - (b) tiger
   - (c) mammal
   - (d) den

5. <u>horse</u> is to <u>stable</u> as <u>bee</u> is to
   - (a) hive
   - (b) insect
   - (c) buzz
   - (d) sting

6. <u>frog</u> is to <u>pond</u> as <u>camel</u> is to
   - (a) lake
   - (b) zebra
   - (c) sea
   - (d) desert

7. <u>ship</u> is to <u>sailor</u> as <u>tent</u> is to
   - (a) house
   - (b) dent
   - (c) camper
   - (d) singer

8. <u>snake</u> is to <u>jungle</u> as <u>dolphin</u> is to
   - (a) ocean
   - (b) tuna
   - (c) fish
   - (d) bush

Analogies © 2002 Creative Teaching Press

Just for Fun
Analogies

Things to Eat

Fill in the bubble next to the word that best completes each analogy.

1. steak is to stake as roll is to
   - (a) ball
   - (b) toll
   - (c) role
   - (d) cookie

2. fruit is to peach as vegetable is to
   - (a) corn
   - (b) dessert
   - (c) candy
   - (d) ice cream

3. apple is to red as carrot is to
   - (a) white
   - (b) orange
   - (c) blue
   - (d) purple

4. lemon is to sour as chocolate is to
   - (a) brown
   - (b) hot
   - (c) dark
   - (d) sweet

5. tomato is to tomatoes as potato is to
   - (a) fruit
   - (b) french fries
   - (c) potatoes
   - (d) vegetable

6. toss is to salad as scramble is to
   - (a) scrambles
   - (b) ramble
   - (c) grape
   - (d) egg

7. flour is to flower as meat is to
   - (a) hamburger
   - (b) fish
   - (c) beef
   - (d) meet

8. milk is to cow as egg is to
   - (a) hen
   - (b) horse
   - (c) camel
   - (d) lamb

Name _____

School Days

Fill in the bubble next to the word that best completes each analogy.

1. <u>plus</u> is to <u>addition</u> as <u>minus</u> is to
   - (a) school
   - (b) numbers
   - (c) division
   - (d) subtraction

2. <u>chalk</u> is to <u>talk</u> as <u>chair</u> is to
   - (a) hair
   - (b) table
   - (c) desk
   - (d) wood

3. <u>quiz</u> is to <u>test</u> as <u>pupil</u> is to
   - (a) ear
   - (b) student
   - (c) boy
   - (d) eye

4. <u>class</u> is to <u>classes</u> as <u>study</u> is to
   - (a) learn
   - (b) homework
   - (c) studys
   - (d) studies

5. <u>true</u> is to <u>false</u> as <u>quiet</u> is to
   - (a) noisy
   - (b) riot
   - (c) quit
   - (d) peaceful

6. <u>read</u> is to <u>book</u> as <u>watch</u> is to
   - (a) hours
   - (b) watches
   - (c) television
   - (d) radio

7. <u>ruler</u> is to <u>measure</u> as <u>scissors</u> is to
   - (a) ink
   - (b) cut
   - (c) knife
   - (d) pen

8. <u>brush</u> is to <u>paint</u> as <u>crayon</u> is to
   - (a) pen
   - (b) draw
   - (c) chalk
   - (d) wax

Things to Wear

Fill in the bubble next to the word that best completes each analogy.

1. <u>cap</u> is to <u>head</u> as <u>glove</u> is to
   - (a) hand
   - (b) dove
   - (c) leather
   - (d) leg

2. <u>sweater</u> is to <u>better</u> as <u>belt</u> is to
   - (a) slacks
   - (b) buckle
   - (c) melt
   - (d) skirt

3. <u>coat</u> is to <u>winter</u> as <u>shorts</u> is to
   - (a) pants
   - (b) keys
   - (c) summer
   - (d) skirt

4. <u>sock</u> is to <u>socks</u> as <u>dress</u> is to
   - (a) coat
   - (b) dresses
   - (c) bonnet
   - (d) jacket

5. <u>boot</u> is to <u>shoe</u> as <u>helmet</u> is to
   - (a) wig
   - (b) shirt
   - (c) slipper
   - (d) hat

6. <u>pajamas</u> is to <u>sleep</u> as <u>uniform</u> is to
   - (a) jeans
   - (b) sweater
   - (c) work
   - (d) suit

7. <u>button</u> is to <u>shirt</u> as <u>zipper</u> is to
   - (a) close
   - (b) scarf
   - (c) pants
   - (d) lace

8. <u>collar</u> is to <u>blouse</u> as <u>pocket</u> is to
   - (a) shirt
   - (b) shoelace
   - (c) tights
   - (d) cleats

Analogies © 2002 Creative Teaching Press

Playtime

Fill in the bubble next to the word that best completes each analogy.

1. jump is to rope as swing is to
   - (a) swim
   - (b) dive
   - (c) skate
   - (d) bat

2. skating is to sport as tulip is to
   - (a) tree
   - (b) flower
   - (c) grass
   - (d) sport

3. club is to golf as stick is to
   - (a) pick
   - (b) hockey
   - (c) soccer
   - (d) basketball

4. ball is to round as book is to
   - (a) rectangular
   - (b) read
   - (c) pages
   - (d) library

5. touchdown is to football as goal is to
   - (a) golf
   - (b) club
   - (c) soccer
   - (d) baseball

6. racket is to jacket as brush is to
   - (a) can
   - (b) rush
   - (c) shrub
   - (d) hurry

7. run is to race as play is to
   - (a) actress
   - (b) work
   - (c) girl
   - (d) game

8. tennis is to court as soccer is to
   - (a) run
   - (b) ball
   - (c) field
   - (d) game

Analogies © 2002 Creative Teaching Press

Measuring, Counting, and Numbers

Fill in the bubble next to the word that best completes each analogy.

1. <u>day</u> is to <u>week</u> as <u>month</u> is to
   - (a) year
   - (b) hour
   - (c) minute
   - (d) yard

2. <u>four</u> is to <u>for</u> as <u>eight</u> is to
   - (a) food
   - (b) eaten
   - (c) ate
   - (d) great

3. <u>Thursday</u> is to <u>day</u> as <u>June</u> is to
   - (a) year
   - (b) second
   - (c) month
   - (d) May

4. <u>ten</u> is to <u>hen</u> as <u>nine</u> is to
   - (a) team
   - (b) add
   - (c) number
   - (d) pine

5. <u>nickel</u> is to <u>five</u> as <u>dime</u> is to
   - (a) quarter
   - (b) penny
   - (c) ten
   - (d) dollar

6. <u>solo</u> is to <u>one</u> as <u>trio</u> is to
   - (a) two
   - (b) three
   - (c) four
   - (d) six

7. <u>first</u> is to <u>last</u> as <u>part</u> is to
   - (a) whole
   - (b) smart
   - (c) party
   - (d) leave

8. <u>foot</u> is to <u>inches</u> as <u>yard</u> is to
   - (a) lawn
   - (b) feet
   - (c) mow
   - (d) card

Analogies © 2002 Creative Teaching Press

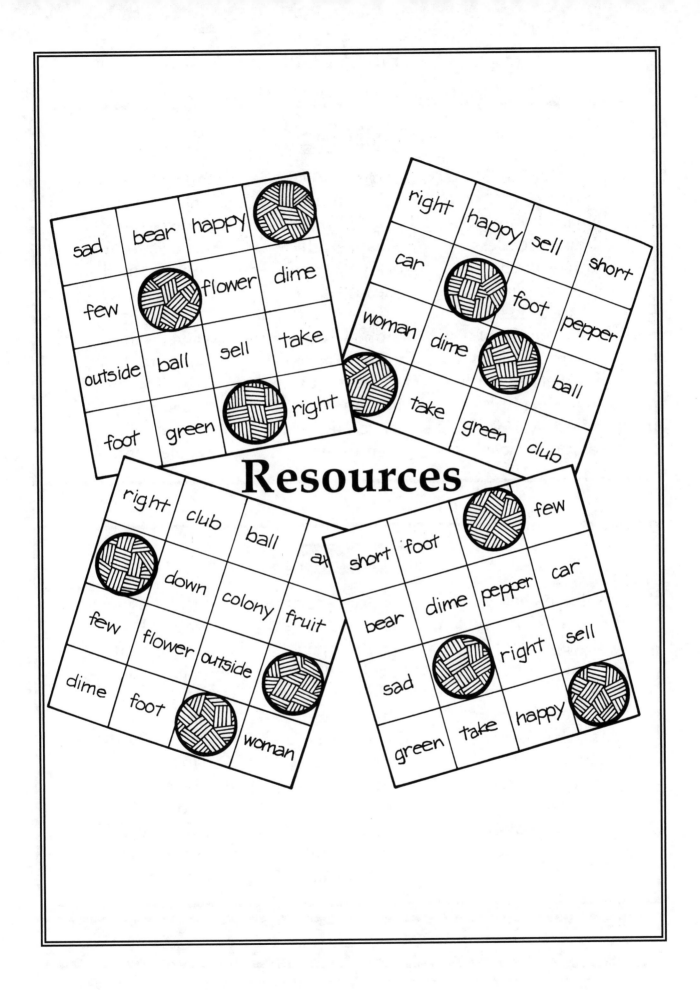

Resources

Word Lists

Synonyms

answer - reply
beg - plead
blank - empty
brave - fearless
buy - purchase
clear - plain
close - near
danger - peril
dense - thick
disappear - vanish
easy - simple
elect - choose
empty - vacant

enemy - rival
false - untrue
fast - quick
fear - fright
forgive - excuse
gleam - shine
grief - sorrow
happen - occur
honest - sincere
ill - sick
imitate - copy
leave - depart
mend - repair

misty - foggy
mix - blend
moist - damp
need - require
odor - smell
pain - ache
piece - part
shiver - shake
silly - foolish
small - tiny
task - job
timid - shy
whole - entire

Antonyms

above - below
absent - present
accept - refuse
alike - different
always - never
appear - vanish
arrive - depart
asleep - awake
attack - defend
back - front
before - after
begin - end
best - worst

bottom - top
clean - dirty
close - open
cold - hot
dark - light
day - night
deep - shallow
down - up
dry - wet
early - late
easy - hard
empty - full
far - near

fast - slow
happy - sad
hard - soft
high - low
kind - cruel
large - small
long - short
lose - win
noisy - quiet
on - off
save - spend
short - tall
wide - narrow

40

Word Lists

Homophones

ad - add	flour - flower	one - won
aisle - isle	for - four	pail - pale
ate - eight	foul - fowl	pair - pear
bare - bear	gait - gate	peace - piece
be - bee	grate - great	peak - peek
beach - beech	groan - grown	peal - peel
beat - beet	hail - hale	plain - plane
been - bin	hair - hare	pole - poll
blew - blue	hall - haul	raise - rays
board - bored	hay - hey	real - reel
bread - bred	heal - heel	road - rode
buy - by	hear - here	sail - sale
cell - sell	heard - herd	scene - seen
cent - sent	hi - high	sea - see
chews - choose	hoarse - horse	seam - seem
creak - creek	hole - whole	sew - so
dear - deer	hour - our	some - sum
die - dye	in - inn	son - sun
do - due - dew	knight - night	stake - steak
doe - dough	knot - not	steal - steel
eye - I	know - no	tail - tale
fair - fare	loan - lone	to - too - two
feat - feet	made - maid	waist - waste
fir - fur	mail - male	weak - week
flea - flee	main - mane	wood - would
flew - flu - flue	meat - meet	yoke - yolk

Analogies © 2002 Creative Teaching Press

Analogy Whizo Game

Instructions for the Teacher

1. For each player, make one copy of the Analogy Whizo Word List (page 43) and one copy of the Analogy Whizo Game Card (page 44).

2. Give each player a word list and a game card.

3. Tell players to write one word from the list in each box on their card. Ask them to pick words from the list at random and cross off each word as they use it so that no word will appear more than once.

4. Give each player a handful of markers (e.g., beans, paper clips, squares of scrap paper).

5. Tell players that they are to listen carefully as you read the first three terms of a four-term analogy. If a word on their card completes the analogy, have players place a marker on the box containing that word.

6. Slowly read each of the analogies listed below in the following form:

   <u>up</u> is to <u>down</u> as <u>hot</u> is to (pause)

   Do not read the last word. Instead, pause to give players a chance to think of the answer and then find and mark it on their card. The last word has been listed so that you can check answers before you declare the winner.

7. Ask the first player to correctly mark four boxes in a row, whether vertically, horizontally, or diagonally, to call out *Whizo!* If the player's answers are correct, declare him or her the winner.

8. For variety, have students play Four-Corner Whizo, L Whizo, 4-Center Whizo, or O Whizo, but remember to identify which variation of Whizo students are going to play before the game begins.

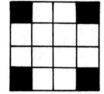 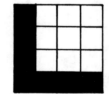 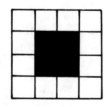 

Analogies to Read Aloud

To further vary the outcome of the game, vary the order in which you read these analogies.
For example, start from the right-hand rather than the left-hand column,
or read from bottom to top rather than from top to bottom.

wet : dry :: give : <u>take</u>	lemon : yellow :: pumpkin : <u>orange</u>
true : false :: buy : <u>sell</u>	finger : hand :: toe : <u>foot</u>
bride : groom :: salt : <u>pepper</u>	front : back :: tall : <u>short</u>
page : book :: petal : <u>flower</u>	sail : ship :: drive : <u>car</u>
lamb : sheep :: cub : <u>bear</u>	high : low :: many : <u>few</u>
hot : cold :: up : <u>down</u>	tennis : racket :: golf : <u>club</u>
glad : happy :: unhappy : <u>sad</u>	carrot : vegetable :: peach : <u>fruit</u>
boy : girl :: man : <u>woman</u>	carpenter : hammer :: firefighter : <u>ax</u>
house : mouse :: kite : <u>right</u>	five : nickel :: ten : <u>dime</u>
calm : peaceful :: fast : <u>quick</u>	ocean : blue :: grass : <u>green</u>
rod : reel :: bat : <u>ball</u>	open : close :: inside : <u>outside</u>
dog : pack :: ant : <u>colony</u>	frightened : scared :: glad : <u>happy</u>

Analogy Whizo Word List

Choose 16 words from the list below. Write one word you have chosen in each box of the Analogy Whizo Game Card. As you choose your words, skip around. Do not copy the words in order. Cross off each word you choose so that you do not write a word on your card more than once.

ax	green
ball	happy
bear	orange
car	outside
club	pepper
colony	quick
dime	right
down	sad
few	sell
flower	short
foot	take
fruit	woman

Analogy Whizo Game Card

First, write one word from the word list in each of the boxes below. Next, listen carefully as your teacher reads an analogy. Then, if the word needed to complete that analogy is on your card, cover it with a marker. When you have covered four squares in a row going up, down, or diagonally, call out "Whizo!" The first player to do so wins the game.

Whizo!

Student Record Sheet

Each time you finish an activity sheet, count the number of correct answers. Color a box for each correct answer by the page number on the left.

Number of Correct Answers

page #	1	2	3	4	5	6	7	8
7								
8								
9								
10								
11								
12								
13								
14								
15								
16								
18								
19								
20								
21								
22								
23								
24								
26								
27								
28								
29								
30								
31								
32								
34								
35								
36								
37								
38								

Name _____

ANALOGY MASTER AWARD

Presented to _____

by _____ on _____

WHIZO WINNER AWARD

Presented to _____

by _____

Analogies © 2002 Creative Teaching Press

Answer Key

Page 7 • Synonyms and Antonyms #1

1. d tardy
2. a closed
3. c new
4. d out
5. b straight
6. d shy
7. c short
8. c nice

Page 8 • Synonyms and Antonyms #2

1. b low
2. a strong
3. d near
4. c different
5. d seek
6. b light
7. d repair
8. c moist

Page 9 • Homophones and Rhyming Words

1. c pale
2. c dog
3. a tide
4. b dew
5. c peace
6. a man
7. b mend
8. b dear

Page 10 • Parts of a Whole and Groupings

1. c choir
2. b bird
3. a troop
4. c camera
5. b shark
6. d hand
7. d leg
8. a key

Page 11 • Characteristics

1. d green
2. b cold
3. c ant
4. a fish
5. a hard
6. b sour
7. d shell
8. c quiet

Page 12 • How Things Are Used/Singular and Plural Spellings

1. c knife
2. d women
3. b boxes
4. c temperature
5. b light
6. c cut
7. d stir
8. b paper

Page 13 • Animal Groups and Offspring

1. b pig
2. d fish
3. a sheep
4. d eaglet
5. d deer
6. b colony
7. c lion
8. b cattle

Page 14 • Tools and Occupations/Things That Go Together

1. c lock
2. a thread
3. b musician
4. b goggles
5. a pepper
6. c jelly
7. c sock
8. b hose

Page 15 • Analogy Review #1

1. d parrot
2. d lead
3. a gas
4. c forest
5. b there
6. d man
7. b dog
8. b dull

Page 16 • Analogy Review #2

1. a boat
2. c ear
3. d problem
4. b separate
5. b nail
6. d range
7. a twelve
8. d shoe

Page 18 • The Human Body

1. a foot
2. d sound
3. c hand
4. b finger
5. c flood
6. d arm
7. b hare
8. a two

Page 19 • The Ocean

1. b beech
2. a quick
3. d gave
4. b bird
5. c wide
6. c green
7. a banana
8. b dance

Page 20 • Fish

1. b human
2. d few
3. b men
4. c flea
5. d bird
6. d peel
7. c kangaroo
8. b pink

Page 21 • Birds

1. c fish
2. b human
3. c black
4. a hive
5. a horse
6. d page
7. c polite
8. b piglet

Analogies © 2002 Creative Teaching Press

Answer Key

Page 22 • Mammals

1. d spots
2. b dog
3. d camel
4. c mice
5. b cave
6. a trunk
7. c tale
8. c lion

Page 23 • Insects

1. b frog
2. c alligator
3. d crow
4. b be
5. c ticket
6. a quick
7. d crawl
8. b roaches

Page 24 • Plants

1. c hand
2. b hem
3. d smell
4. a fruit
5. b line
6. d leg
7. d ocean
8. c brush

Page 26 • In the Neighborhood

1. b baseball
2. c track
3. a lady
4. b messy
5. d house
6. c paper
7. d bank
8. a loose

Page 27 • Community Helpers

1. c thermometer
2. d shut
3. c school
4. b computer
5. c fudge
6. a flowers
7. d animals
8. b part

Page 28 • Transportation

1. d far
2. a sky
3. b plane
4. d leave
5. c airplane
6. c motorcycle
7. a bicycle
8. b buses

Page 29 • Communication

1. c seem
2. c computer
3. b radio
4. a box
5. a babies
6. b listen
7. c blow
8. d football

Page 30 • Geography

1. d west
2. a tired
3. c take
4. c sent
5. d state
6. a so
7. a word
8. b cold

Page 31 • Seasons and Celebrations

1. b spring
2. d February
3. d yellow
4. b whole
5. a knight
6. c choir
7. a face
8. d winter

Page 32 • Homes

1. c logs
2. c jacket
3. b river
4. d den
5. a hive
6. d desert
7. c camper
8. a ocean

Page 34 • Things to Eat

1. c role
2. a corn
3. b orange
4. d sweet
5. c potatoes
6. d egg
7. d meet
8. a hen

Page 35 • School Days

1. d subtraction
2. a hair
3. b student
4. d studies
5. a noisy
6. c television
7. b cut
8. b draw

Page 36 • Things to Wear

1. a hand
2. c melt
3. c summer
4. b dresses
5. d hat
6. c work
7. c pants
8. a shirt

Page 37 • Playtime

1. d bat
2. b flower
3. b hockey
4. a rectangular
5. c soccer
6. b rush
7. d game
8. c field

Page 38 • Measuring, Counting, and Numbers

1. a year
2. c ate
3. c month
4. d pine
5. c ten
6. b three
7. a whole
8. b feet

Analogies © 2002 Creative Teaching Press